THE FIRES OF WAR AND PASSION ENFLAME THE EMOTIONS OF A YOUNG AMERICA.

RENNO—Born a white man, raised a Seneca, the revered Sachem of the invincible Iroquois must face a devastating choice: to fight for his nation —but against his own blood.

JA-GONH—Mighty son of the great Renno, he has passed the Seneca's skill and stealth on to his only child. Now he faces deadly combat with the very son he bore.

GHONKABA—Renno's warrior grandson. In him is reborn the impetuous spirit of the White Indian's youth. His rebellious nature can make him a dangerous traitor or perhaps the greatest Seneca of them all.

ELIZABETH STRONG—Lovely blond daughter of a Colonial general, her love can make Ghonkaba a loyal friend of the colonists; her betrayal can make him a bitter foe.

GEORGE WASHINGTON—As a valiant colonel in the Virginia militia, his prowess and daring win him Ghonkaba's brotherhood. But other powerful colonists reveal a dark side of the white man's world.

The White Indian Series
Ask your bookseller for the books you have missed

The White Indian Series
Book VII

WAR CRY

Donald Clayton Porter

BCI

Created by the producers of
Wagons West, Children of the Lion,
Saga of the Southwest, and
The Kent Family Chronicles Series.

Executive Producer: Lyle Kenyon Engel

BANTAM BOOKS
TORONTO • NEW YORK • LONDON • SYDNEY

WAR CRY

A Bantam Book / published by arrangement with
Book Creations, Inc.
Bantam edition / February 1983

Produced by Book Creations, Inc.
Executive Producer: Lyle Kenyon Engel

All rights reserved.
Copyright © 1983 by Book Creations, Inc.
Illustrations by Clay Ghiosay.
Cover art copyright © 1983 by Lou Glanzman.
This book may not be reproduced in whole or in part, by
mimeograph or any other means, without permission.
For information address: Bantam Books, Inc.

ISBN 0-553-23022-0

Published simultaneously in the United States and Canada

PRINTED IN THE UNITED STATES OF AMERICA

H   0 9 8 7 6 5 4 3 2 1

WAR CRY

Chapter I

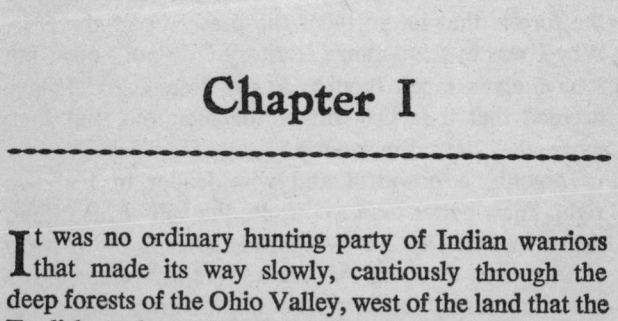

It was no ordinary hunting party of Indian warriors that made its way slowly, cautiously through the deep forests of the Ohio Valley, west of the land that the English settlers called Pennsylvania, and north of the Ohio River. Rarely did as many as fifty braves take part simultaneously in a hunt.

That their green and yellow war paint identified them as Seneca warriors was highly unusual because these Seneca were far from their own land in the northern portion of New York. And a closer scrutiny revealed other unusual aspects of the party.

The leader was white-haired with a wrinkled face,

1

but his still-slender body and erect carriage belied his more than eighty summers. Renno, the white Indian and Great Sachem of the Iroquois League, the most powerful of all Indian alliances in North America, was a legend in his own time. Renowned and respected by the English colonists, he was feared by the French and their Indian allies. His own Seneca believed him to have almost godlike qualities, and he was seen as a larger-than-life leader by most other Indian nations.

Seldom did the Seneca venture so far from home. But it was Renno's wish to make such a journey, and as usual, his orders were obeyed to the letter.

"I dreamed a strange dream," he had told his son, Ja-gonh, sachem of the Seneca, several days earlier. "I went to the lands where the Miami nation roams, to the forests that lie north of the preserves of the Erie. Why I was in this strange territory I do not know, but I have given much thought to my dream, and I have decided that it is the will of the manitous that I go where they have directed me."

Ja-gonh, a powerful and wise leader in his own right, knew better than to dispute the will of his father. As he had said to Ah-wen-ga, his wife, in the privacy of their own dwelling that night, "As my father grows older, his resemblance to Ghonka, my grandfather, becomes more and more pronounced. He is so accustomed to having his word obeyed in all things that he tolerates no argument and no discussion. When he told me that it was his wish to hunt in the distant land of the Ohio, I assigned fifty senior warriors as his bodyguard, and I gave command of the party to Ghonkaba, our son."

"I can't imagine why Renno would wish to hunt so far from his home," Ah-wen-ga had replied in some wonder. "Surely the deer are no larger and fatter than the deer that live here in our own forests. Why does Renno insist on going into an alien land?"

"He has traveled to Quebec and other places in Canada to the north," Ja-gonh had pointed out. "He has often visited Virginia, the home of my mother, and in his travels, he has gone far beyond the land of the Seminole, in the land the Spaniards call Florida, to the islands of the West Indian Ocean. He has visited at length in England as well. As his life draws nearer to its close on this earth, I suspect he is filled with a desire to visit a new region that he has not previously known."

Ah-wen-ga, who was still as pretty as the day some twenty-five years earlier when she had been abducted to France by enemies of the Seneca, nodded in accord. "It well may be that Ja-gonh is right."

"It is the privilege of my father," Ja-gonh had said solemnly, "to go where he wishes and to do there what pleases him. I have fulfilled my obligations to him by sending our most courageous and talented warriors with him, under the command of my own son, and may his exploits someday be as great as those of the famous ancestor whose name he bears."

As it happened, Ja-gonh's son was bored by his assignment. He recognized the honor of being placed in charge of the warriors responsible for the safety of his famous grandfather, but that fact in no way compensated for the annoyances of day-to-day travel. The pace of the hunt, due to Renno's advanced age, was almost infuriatingly leisurely for a hot-blooded young brave who still was eager to make his mark in the world.

But what was really bothering Ghonkaba was some-

3

thing he would admit to no one. He had lived his entire life in the shadow of renowned warriors, first his namesake, Ghonka the Elder, sachem of the Seneca, then Great Sachem of the Iroquois League—a warrior beyond compare. After Ghonka had come his adopted son, Renno, whose accomplishments almost miraculously had equaled—and sometimes even surpassed—those of Ghonka himself. Now it was Ja-gonh who wore the feathered headdress and cape of sachem of the Seneca.

Ghonkaba knew that the entire nation was expecting him to perform in both war and in peace with valor and sagacity at least equal to any of them. All his life, Ghonkaba had stood apart from his contemporaries, and was considered "different." Unlike his grandfather and his father, who were both white skinned, he was a half-breed. Thanks to the Indian blood of his mother, Ah-wen-ga, he was the first in the family since Ghonka who could truly call himself a Seneca. Yet the nation, its Iroquois allies, the white settlers in Massachusetts Bay, Connecticut, and New York—and even the tribes that were enemies of the Seneca—looked to him for great deeds, not only because of his distinguished heritage, but particularly because of his name: Ghonka the Younger.

How often Renno and Ja-gonh had lectured him: "Mighty deeds are required of a Seneca warrior simply because he is a Seneca. Your standards are still higher because you are of the family of Ghonka and of Renno."

Even his grandfather on his mother's side, Sun-ai-yee, a renowned war chief, had achieved great distinction as sachem of the nation. Ghonkaba more than once found himself wishing that he could escape the magnificent aura that surrounded him.

With difficulty, Ghonkaba was forcing himself to keep his mind on his task as he crept through the thick forest several paces to the left of Renno. The rest of the escort were strung out over several hundred feet to the right and to the left—all of them invisible from a distance of only a few paces. As a Seneca, Ghonkaba took such accomplishments for granted. The warriors of no other nation could have traveled so silently through the deep underbrush, nor could they have maintained as high a degree of invisibility thanks to the disciplined, rigorous training that the Seneca received from earliest boyhood.

Suddenly Renno halted and, leaning forward silently, peered intently through the thick foliage.

Ghonkaba stopped abruptly and signaled for the entire column to come to a halt. He could see nothing, but he assumed that Renno had perhaps caught a glimpse of a deer or some other animal that he, with his now sometimes unreliable eyesight, imagined to be a deer.

Renno reached over his shoulder for an arrow that he inserted with practiced ease to his bow, then fired; Ghonkaba followed its flight almost indolently, but suddenly he snapped to full attention. No more than thirty paces ahead of them was a brave wearing the purple and white war paint of the Erie, a nation long an enemy of the Seneca.

Before the young warrior could intervene, Renno fired a second arrow, then a third. It seemed to Ghonkaba at first that Renno was missing his target, but he quickly realized that his grandfather's aim was as accurate as it had ever been. One arrow buried itself in a

5

tree trunk scant inches ahead of the Erie, a second pierced another tree directly behind him, and a third dropped to the ground at his feet. He was surrounded by Seneca fire, yet was unharmed and untouched.

A ring of authority entered Renno's voice as he declared softly, "Ghonkaba! Take some of the escort with you and make the Erie brave your prisoner. Do not harm him in any way; just bring him to me."

Hastening to obey the order, Ghonkaba told himself that he was on a fool's errand. Had he been fortunate enough to see the Erie first, he would have put a tomahawk into him and added a scalp to those he carried in his belt. His grandfather, he decided, must be growing soft.

Signaling to several of his comrades, Ghonkaba advanced stealthily but rapidly through the forest. The other Seneca did the same, spreading out as they moved, and in a classic maneuver, they succeeded in surrounding the Erie. The warrior, apparently having realized that he was being warned to halt, did not move as he tried to determine his best course of action, when four Seneca appeared, seemingly out of nowhere, only a few feet away.

The Erie, a man of courage, was not foolhardy, and recognizing that a fight against such odds would be futile and probably fatal, he surrendered without a struggle.

Ghonkaba, his thoughts hidden behind his impassive face, led the captive back to his grandfather.

As always in dealing with fellow Indians, regardless of their tribes, Renno was courteous. "I am Renno of the Seneca," he said, "and if you answer my questions truthfully, you will not suffer. But hear me well, O Erie—evade the truth, and you will not live!"

The Erie stared in undisguised astonishment at the white-haired man who stood before him with his arms folded across his chest. Quick to recognize the war paint of the dreaded Seneca, the brave knew the identity of his captor, the renowned Renno, by his piercing blue eyes and suntanned pale skin. What could he be doing so far from his own land?

"Why are you in the land of the Miami?" Renno demanded, his voice soft, even gentle, though he carried himself with such authority that the Erie cringed.

"I was sent as a messenger to the sachem of the Miami," he replied.

"How does it happen," Renno continued, "that the French, who live far to the north in Canada, have chosen to employ a brave of the Erie as their messenger?"

Staring in surprise, Ghonkaba wondered—not for the first time—whether his grandfather was clairvoyant. How could he have known that the Erie was in the employ of France?

The prisoner, taking seriously the warning of the Great Sachem of the Iroquois, decided to be truthful. "The Erie," he said, "have now become the allies of France."

This was news—startling and totally unexpected—and Ghonkaba and the other warriors nearby were stunned.

But Renno, showing neither surprise nor emotion, directed an order to the captive. "Give me the pouch that contains messages sent by the French to the sachem of the Miami," he commanded.

The Erie silently unwound the thong of a leather pouch at his waist and handed it over.

At least one mystery was solved, Ghonkaba thought,

as he recognized that burned into the rawhide pouch was the faint but unmistakable symbol of the fleur-de-lis, the emblem of France. To his grandfather, it had been a telltale indication that the brave was a French messenger, and Ghonkaba now felt slightly abashed for having doubted Renno's eyesight. Extraordinary all his long life, it was still superior to almost anyone else's.

Renno opened the pouch and unrolled a parchment scroll containing a message written in French and, below it, a translation into the language of the Algonquian, a large tribe that was a traditional ally of France.

Dated no more than two months earlier, in April 1755, the document was signed by the Marquis Louis Joseph de Montcalm de Veran. Renno knew of General Montcalm as the military commander in chief of the armies of King Louis XV of France in the New World.

The message itself was a simple one: France was engaged in a great crusade to drive the English colonists out of North America for all time. With him in this grand design were several large and powerful Indian nations, among them the Algonquian and Huron, the Ottawa and the Erie. The Miami were being invited to join in the alliance. In return for their fealty to France, they would be supplied with the most modern French firearms and ample ammunition. French military instructors would be sent to teach them how to use these remarkable weapons.

And even greater benefits could await the Miami in an alliance with France. The nations of the Iroquois League, as allies of the British colonists, would be a principal object of the campaign. Once the Iroquois were defeated, their lands would be confiscated and would be shared by the victorious Indian nations. Though the message said nothing about the fate of the people of the Iroquois, tradition dictated that any who were not killed in combat would be enslaved.

Renno felt a deep dismay as he read the invitation to the Miami. Almost all his adult life had involved warfare against the French; he had taken part in several major campaigns. In a significant way, his reputation rested on his achievements in those campaigns. Now France, still ambitious and greedy, was planning on a new attempt to drive the British out of their seaboard colonies and to annihilate their Iroquois comrades.

Renno was discouraged and weary. But suddenly blood started coursing rapidly through his veins again. The cause for which he had fought so long and honorably was coming to life again, and now his people were threatened by danger. The Seneca and the other nations of the Iroquois needed him, and he would have to respond to the challenge without delay.

Impatient throughout the exchange, Ghonkaba was relieved to see that it seemed to be nearing an end. Now, he thought, the Erie would be turned over to him, and he could dispose of the brave promptly and add a scalp to his belt.

But his grandfather surprised and dismayed him again. "If I were to follow the custom of the wilderness," Renno told the captive, "I would hand you over to these warriors and allow them to deal with you as they please."

The Erie warrior's face fell in horror. "On this occasion, however," Renno went on, "I shall spare your life."

Ghonkaba was disgusted. His grandfather was becoming soft and senile, he felt, but he could do nothing.

"You will return to the land of the Erie without delay," Renno instructed the warrior. "I assume you are not the only messenger who was sent by your sachem to the Miami."

The Erie swallowed hard. This aged Seneca had an uncanny ability to read his mind. "I was but one of several couriers sent to the Miami," he acknowledged. "Three others were given the same assignment."

"You will relate to the sachem of the Erie and to the elders of his council what has befallen you in the wilderness," Renno now instructed. "Then you will give them a special message from Renno of the Seneca, Great Sachem of all the Iroquois. You will remind your listeners that they have been enemies of the Seneca from the time when my father's father was very young. Many times through the long years the Erie have broken the peace with the Seneca. Each time they have resorted to arms, they have lost. Their warriors, the cream of their nation, have been killed in battle, their squaws and their children enslaved and forced to work for the Seneca until the end of their days.

"Unfortunately, the Erie seem to have learned nothing from their tragic experiences," he went on. "You will tell the sachem and the council of the Erie to listen to the words of Renno of the Seneca and to heed his advice. The Seneca and the Erie are now at peace. The Erie are free to hunt and fish where they please, their women grow bountiful crops, and their children grow strong and sturdy. But if the Erie once again break the peace, all that will change. This time, the Seneca will grind them into the dust as kernels of corn are ground at the bottom of a bowl to create the dust from which